Paul Harris: Simultaneous Learning

CW00407918

the complete

Musicians' Union
mu

Practice Workbook

| Name |
| Address |
| |
| Teacher |

FABER *ff* MUSIC

Character

✓

Improvising

✓

Keys/Scales

Listening

Memory

Performing

✓

Posture

Rhythm

✓

Sight reading

Technique

✓

Theory

Other

Lesson highlights, achievements and key points

You really found the character of Minuet in F.
Think light!

Lesson date

12/2

Main focus for practice

Think: key – rhythms – lifting notes – building phrases

Find a Minuet online (preferably danced in period costume!)

Play and imagine!

Think about the structure of the Minuet and begin to make up Minuet-like improvisations.

Reflections on my practice

What went well?

Thinking in the key. Really got it!
Enjoyed exploring the Minuet structure.

Any problems?

Still need more help on those lifted notes.

General updates, activities and things to mention in the next lesson

Found a great site that has explanations of dances (with dancing).

Played duets with friend all Sunday afternoon!

In this space, use your imagination to reflect on one of your pieces:
write a poem, draw a picture, create a colour scape – whatever you want!

This jolly dance
Goes one, two and three.
It's in the key of F;
Will you step in time with me?

1 2 3 1 2 3 1 2 3

What I need to bring to the next lesson

• *Minuet*

• *Website address for minuets*

• *Duets*

Simultaneous Learning Practice Map

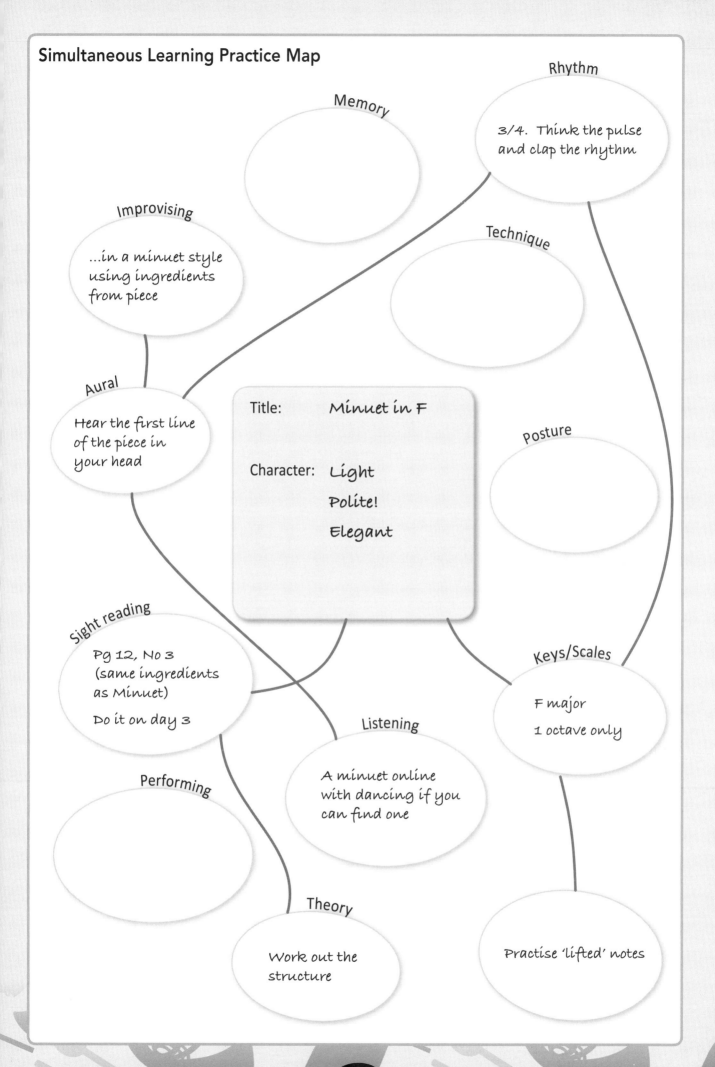

Rhythm

3/4. Think the pulse and clap the rhythm

Memory

Improvising

...in a minuet style using ingredients from piece

Technique

Aural

Hear the first line of the piece in your head

Title: Minuet in F

Character: Light
Polite!
Elegant

Posture

Sight reading

Pg 12, No 3 (same ingredients as Minuet)

Do it on day 3

Keys/Scales

F major
1 octave only

Listening

A minuet online with dancing if you can find one

Performing

Theory

Work out the structure

Practise 'lifted' notes

Lesson highlights, achievements and key points

Lesson date

Main focus for practice

Reflections on my practice

What went well?

General updates, activities and things to mention in the next lesson

Any problems?

In this space, use your imagination to reflect on one of your pieces: write a poem, draw a picture, create a colour scape – whatever you want!

What I need to bring to the next lesson

Simultaneous Learning Practice Map

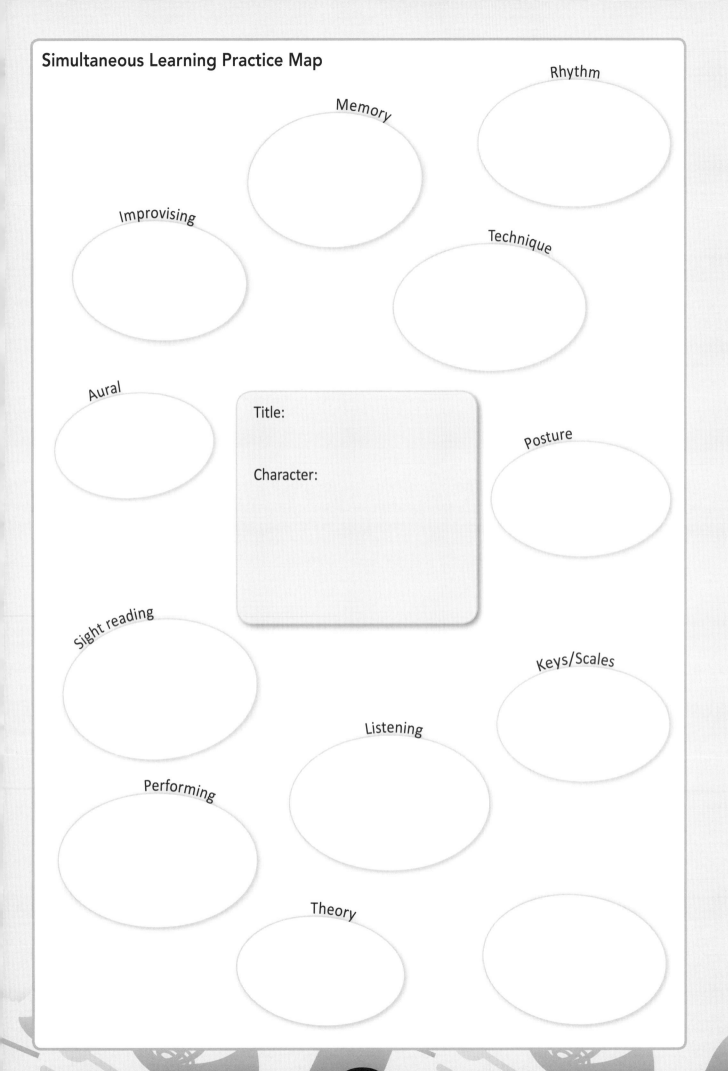

Rhythm

Memory

Improvising

Technique

Aural

Title:

Character:

Posture

Sight reading

Keys/Scales

Listening

Performing

Theory

Aural

Character

Improvising

Keys/Scales

Listening

Memory

Performing

Posture

Rhythm

Sight reading

Technique

Theory

Other

Lesson highlights, achievements and key points

Lesson date

Main focus for practice

Reflections on my practice

What went well?

Any problems?

General updates, activities and things to mention in the next lesson

In this space, use your imagination to reflect on one of your pieces:
write a poem, draw a picture, create a colour scape – whatever you want!

What I need to bring to the next lesson

Simultaneous Learning Practice Map

Rhythm

Memory

Improvising

Technique

Aural

Title:

Character:

Posture

Sight reading

Keys/Scales

Listening

Performing

Theory

Aural

Character

Improvising

Keys/Scales

Listening

Memory

Performing

Posture

Rhythm

Sight reading

Technique

Theory

Other

Lesson highlights, achievements and key points

Lesson date

Main focus for practice

Reflections on my practice

What went well?

Any problems?

General updates, activities and things to mention in the next lesson

In this space, use your imagination to reflect on one of your pieces: write a poem, draw a picture, create a colour scape – whatever you want!

What I need to bring to the next lesson

Simultaneous Learning Practice Map

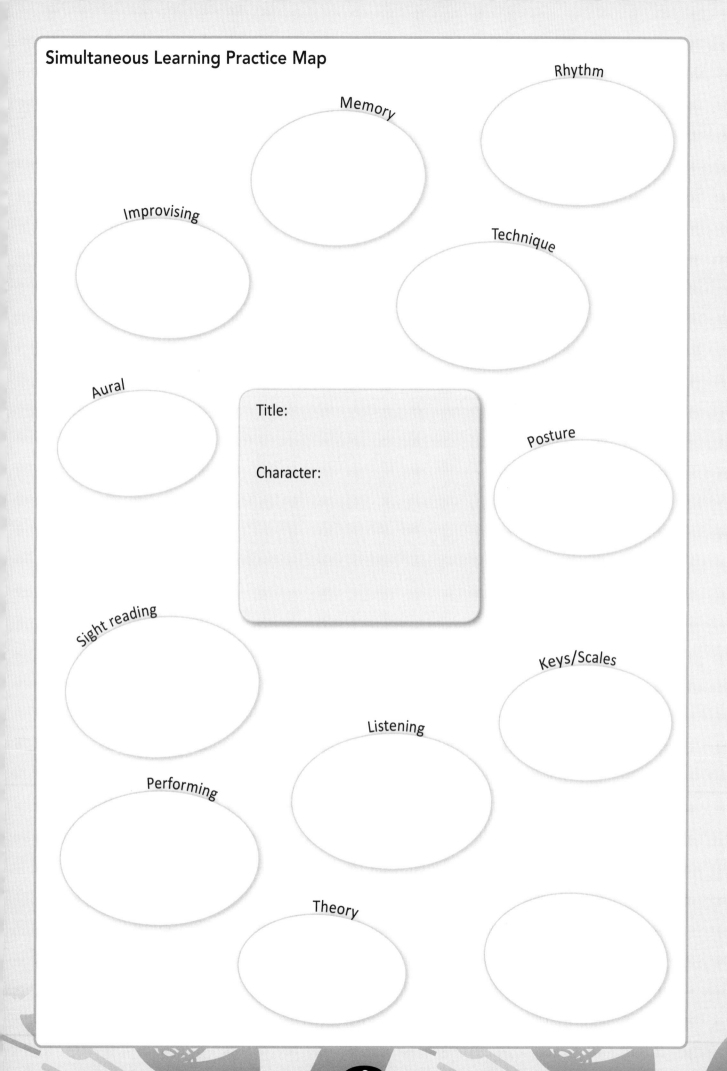

Rhythm

Memory

Improvising

Technique

Aural

Title:

Character:

Posture

Sight reading

Keys/Scales

Listening

Performing

Theory

Lesson highlights, achievements and key points

Lesson date

Main focus for practice

Reflections on my practice

What went well?

Any problems?

General updates, activities and things to mention in the next lesson

In this space, use your imagination to reflect on one of your pieces:
write a poem, draw a picture, create a colour scape – whatever you want!

What I need to bring to the next lesson

Simultaneous Learning Practice Map

Rhythm

Memory

Improvising

Technique

Aural

Title:

Character:

Posture

Sight reading

Keys/Scales

Listening

Performing

Theory

Aural

Character

Improvising

Keys/Scales

Listening

Memory

Performing

Posture

Rhythm

Sight reading

Technique

Theory

Other

Lesson highlights, achievements and key points

Lesson date

Main focus for practice

Reflections on my practice

What went well?

Any problems?

General updates, activities and things to mention in the next lesson

In this space, use your imagination to reflect on one of your pieces:
write a poem, draw a picture, create a colour scape – whatever you want!

What I need to bring to the next lesson

Simultaneous Learning Practice Map

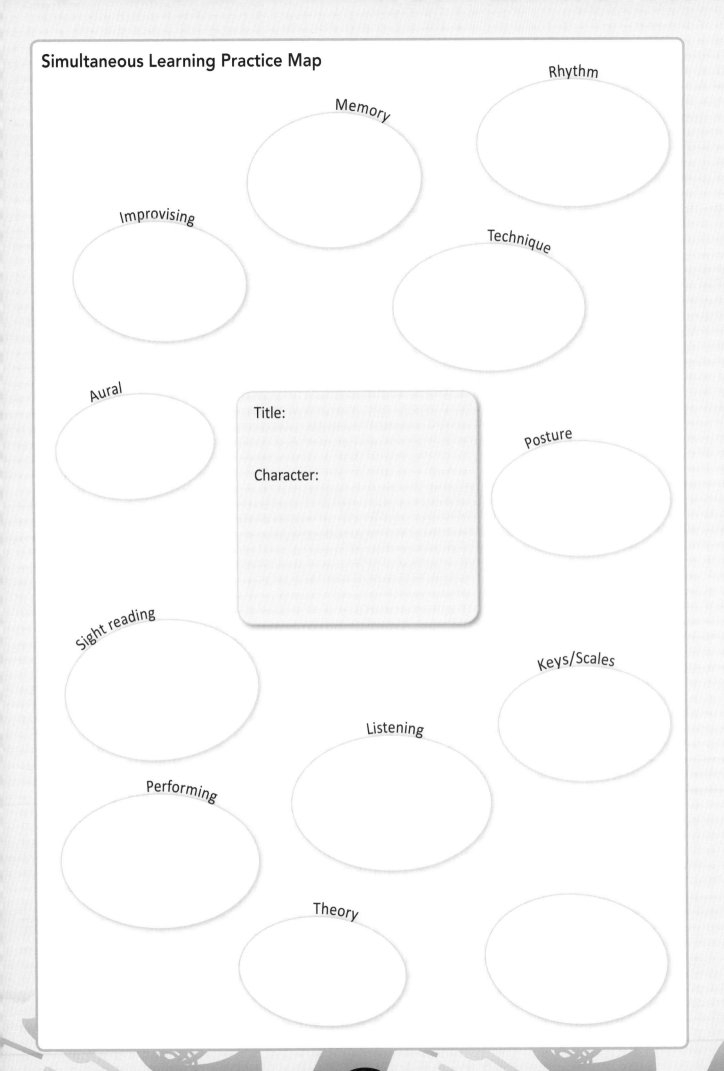

Rhythm

Memory

Improvising

Technique

Aural

Title:

Character:

Posture

Sight reading

Keys/Scales

Listening

Performing

Theory

Lesson highlights, achievements and key points

Lesson date

Main focus for practice

Reflections on my practice

What went well?

Any problems?

General updates, activities and things to mention in the next lesson

In this space, use your imagination to reflect on one of your pieces:
write a poem, draw a picture, create a colour scape – whatever you want!

What I need to bring to the next lesson

Simultaneous Learning Practice Map

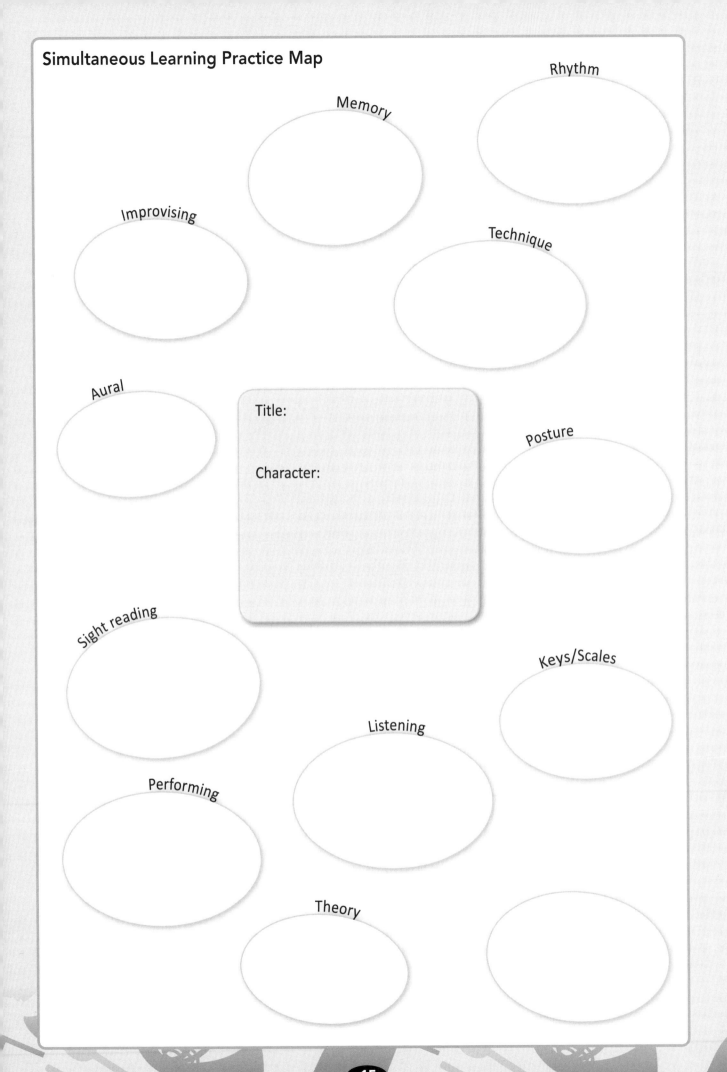

Rhythm

Memory

Improvising

Technique

Aural

Title:

Character:

Posture

Sight reading

Keys/Scales

Listening

Performing

Theory

Aural

Character

Improvising

Keys/Scales

Listening

Memory

Performing

Posture

Rhythm

Sight reading

Technique

Theory

Other

Lesson highlights, achievements and key points

Lesson date

Main focus for practice

Reflections on my practice

What went well?

Any problems?

General updates, activities and things to mention in the next lesson

In this space, use your imagination to reflect on one of your pieces: write a poem, draw a picture, create a colour scape – whatever you want!

What I need to bring to the next lesson

Simultaneous Learning Practice Map

Memory

Rhythm

Improvising

Technique

Aural

Title:

Character:

Posture

Sight reading

Keys/Scales

Listening

Performing

Theory

Aural

Character

Improvising

Keys/Scales

Listening

Memory

Performing

Posture

Rhythm

Sight reading

Technique

Theory

Other

Lesson highlights, achievements and key points

Lesson date

Main focus for practice

Reflections on my practice

What went well?

Any problems?

General updates, activities and things to mention in the next lesson

In this space, use your imagination to reflect on one of your pieces: write a poem, draw a picture, create a colour scape – whatever you want!

What I need to bring to the next lesson

Simultaneous Learning Practice Map

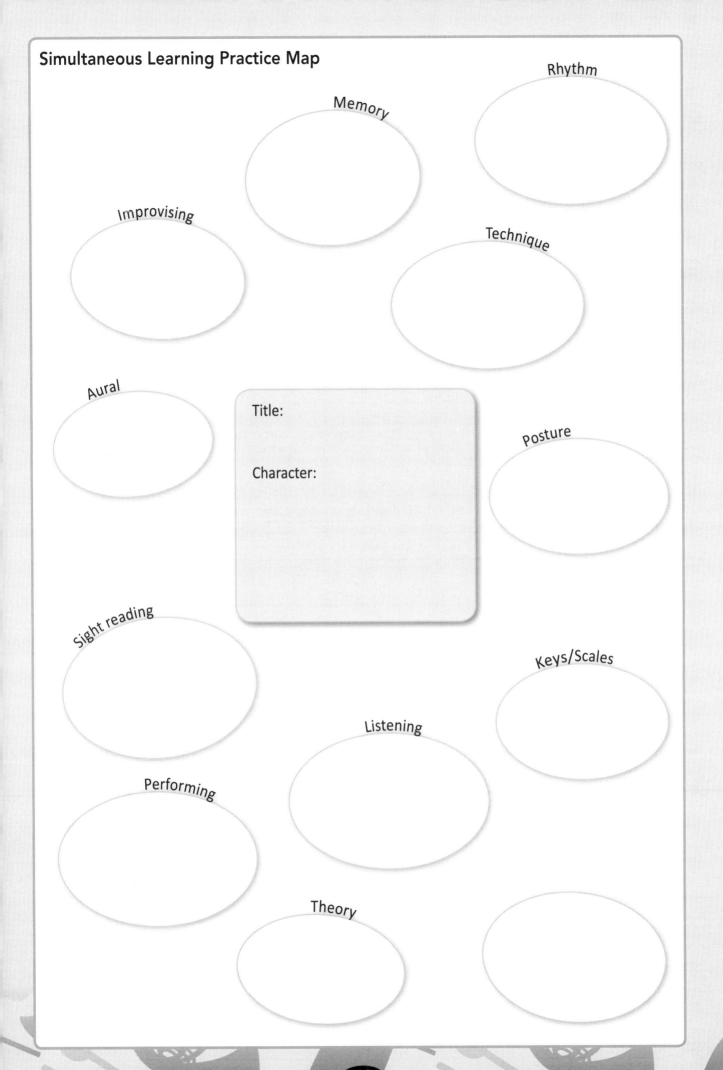

Memory

Rhythm

Improvising

Technique

Aural

Title:

Character:

Posture

Sight reading

Keys/Scales

Listening

Performing

Theory

Aural

Character

Improvising

Keys/Scales

Listening

Memory

Performing

Posture

Rhythm

Sight reading

Technique

Theory

Other

Lesson highlights, achievements and key points

Lesson date

Main focus for practice

Reflections on my practice

What went well?

Any problems?

General updates, activities and things to mention in the next lesson

In this space, use your imagination to reflect on one of your pieces:
write a poem, draw a picture, create a colour scape – whatever you want!

What I need to bring to the next lesson

Simultaneous Learning Practice Map

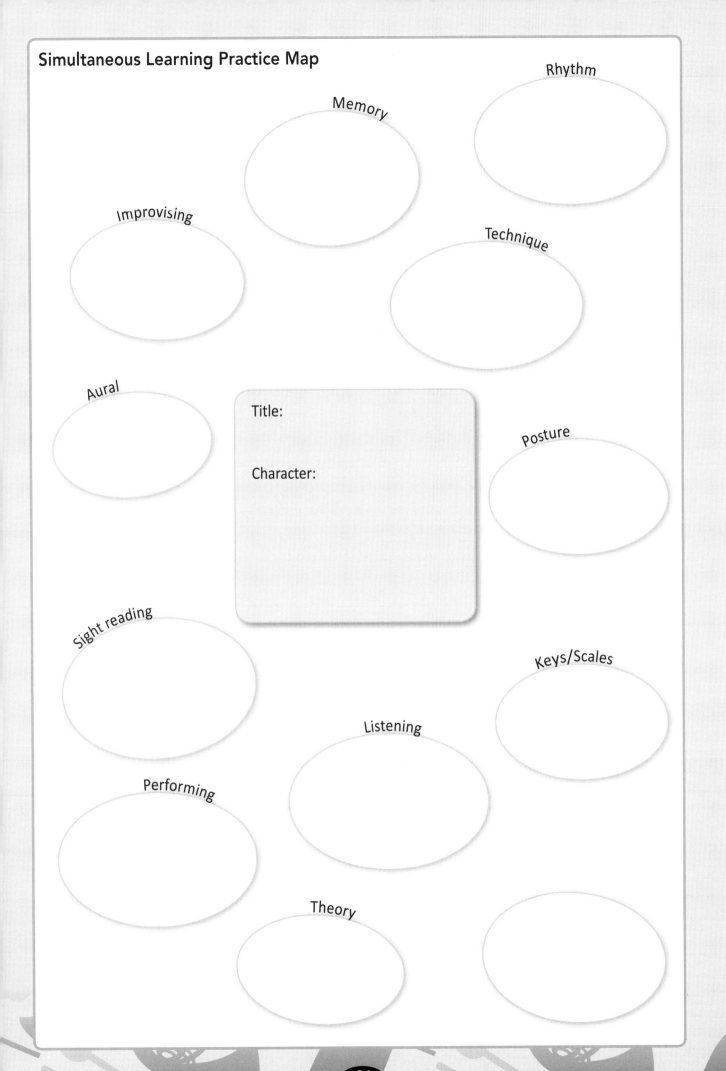

Rhythm

Memory

Improvising

Technique

Aural

Title:

Character:

Posture

Sight reading

Keys/Scales

Listening

Performing

Theory

Aural

Character

Improvising

Keys/Scales

Listening

Memory

Performing

Posture

Rhythm

Sight reading

Technique

Theory

Other

Lesson highlights, achievements and key points

Lesson date

Main focus for practice

Reflections on my practice

What went well?

Any problems?

General updates, activities and things to mention in the next lesson

In this space, use your imagination to reflect on one of your pieces:
write a poem, draw a picture, create a colour scape – whatever you want!

What I need to bring to the next lesson

Simultaneous Learning Practice Map

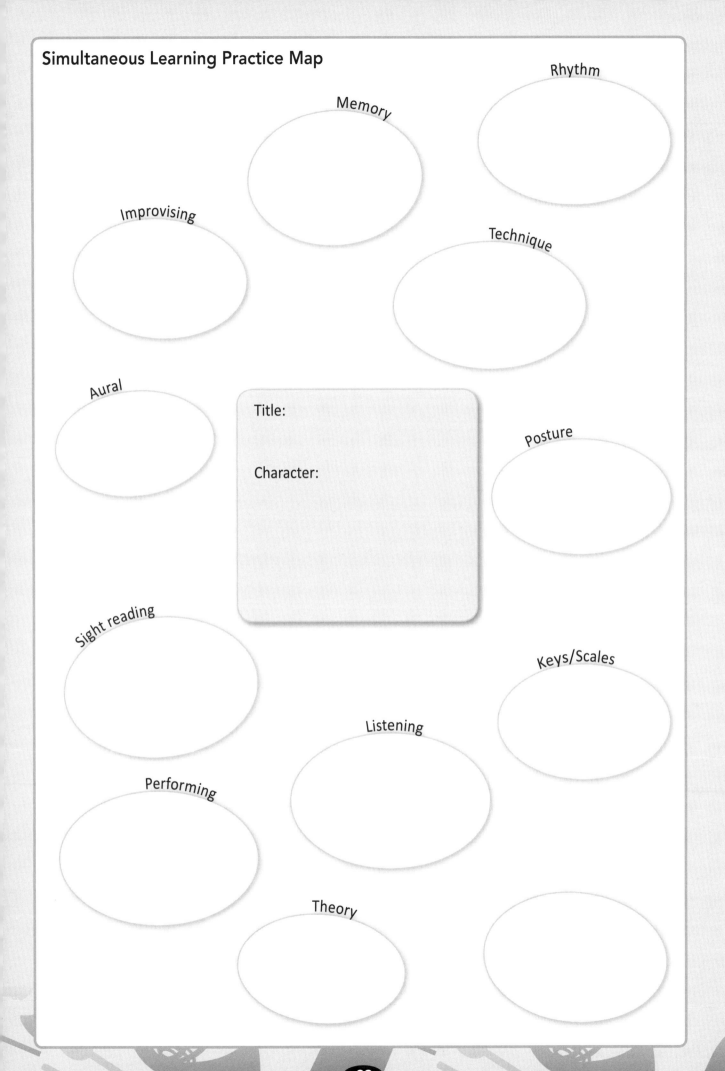

Rhythm

Memory

Improvising

Technique

Aural

Title:

Character:

Posture

Sight reading

Keys/Scales

Listening

Performing

Theory

Aural

Character

Improvising

Keys/Scales

Listening

Memory

Performing

Posture

Rhythm

Sight reading

Technique

Theory

Other

Lesson highlights, achievements and key points

Lesson date

Main focus for practice

Reflections on my practice

What went well?

Any problems?

General updates, activities and things to mention in the next lesson

In this space, use your imagination to reflect on one of your pieces:
write a poem, draw a picture, create a colour scape – whatever you want!

What I need to bring to the next lesson

Simultaneous Learning Practice Map

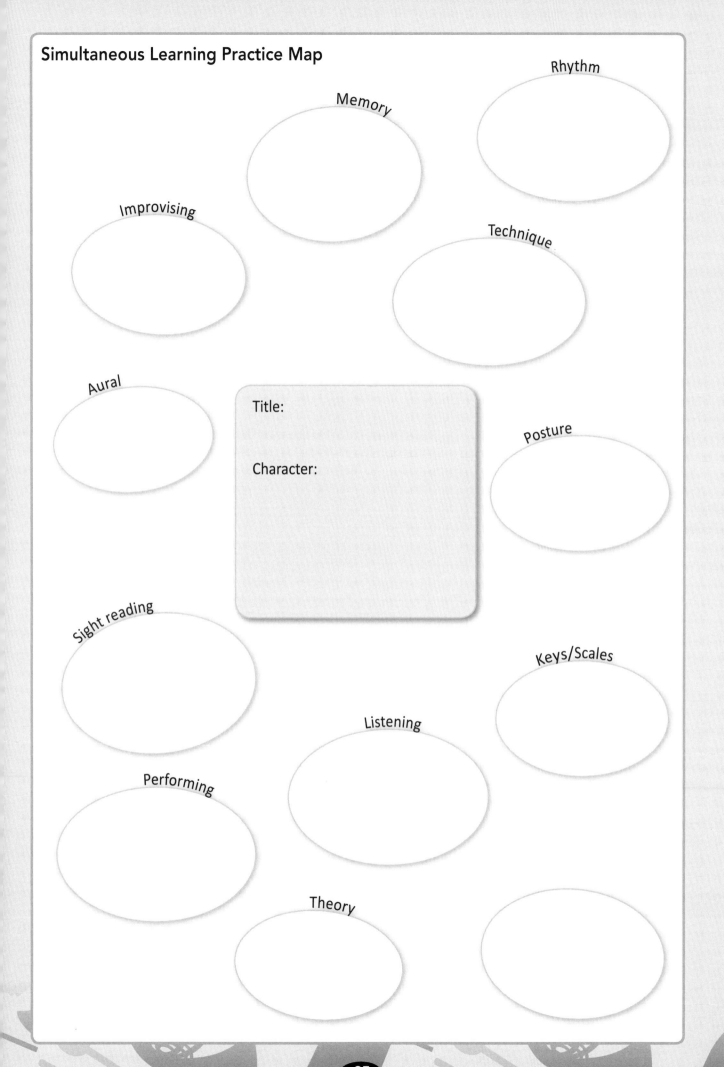

Rhythm

Memory

Improvising

Technique

Aural

Title:

Character:

Posture

Sight reading

Keys/Scales

Listening

Performing

Theory

Lesson highlights, achievements and key points

Lesson date

Main focus for practice

Reflections on my practice

What went well?

Any problems?

General updates, activities and things to mention in the next lesson

In this space, use your imagination to reflect on one of your pieces:
write a poem, draw a picture, create a colour scape – whatever you want!

What I need to bring to the next lesson

Simultaneous Learning Practice Map

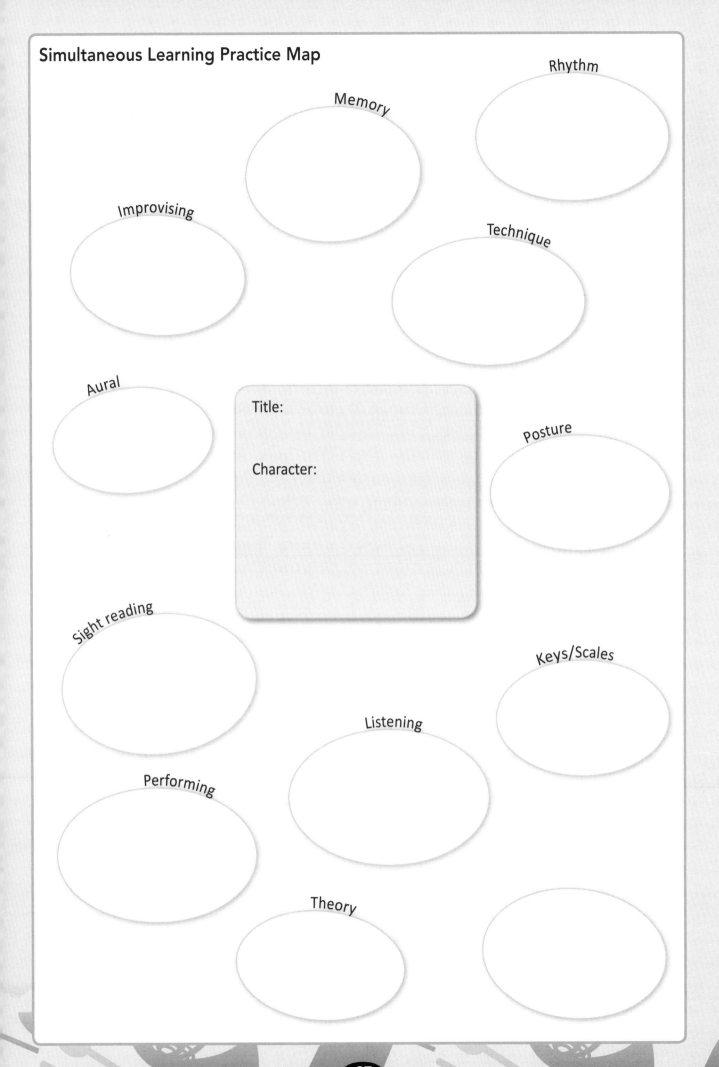

Rhythm

Memory

Improvising

Technique

Aural

Title:

Character:

Posture

Sight reading

Keys/Scales

Listening

Performing

Theory

Lesson highlights, achievements and key points

Lesson date

Main focus for practice

Reflections on my practice

What went well?

Any problems?

General updates, activities and things to mention in the next lesson

In this space, use your imagination to reflect on one of your pieces:
write a poem, draw a picture, create a colour scape – whatever you want!

What I need to bring to the next lesson

Simultaneous Learning Practice Map

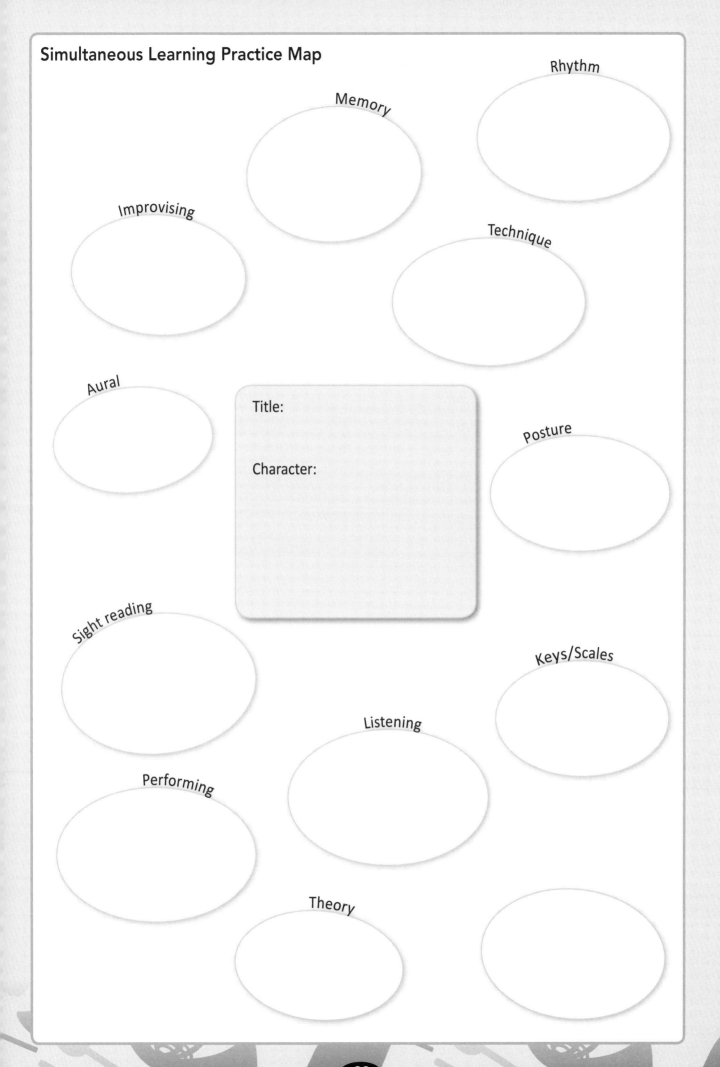

Memory

Rhythm

Improvising

Technique

Aural

Title:

Character:

Posture

Sight reading

Keys/Scales

Listening

Performing

Theory

Lesson highlights, achievements and key points

Lesson date

Main focus for practice

Reflections on my practice

What went well?

Any problems?

General updates, activities and things to mention in the next lesson

In this space, use your imagination to reflect on one of your pieces:
write a poem, draw a picture, create a colour scape – whatever you want!

What I need to bring to the next lesson

Simultaneous Learning Practice Map

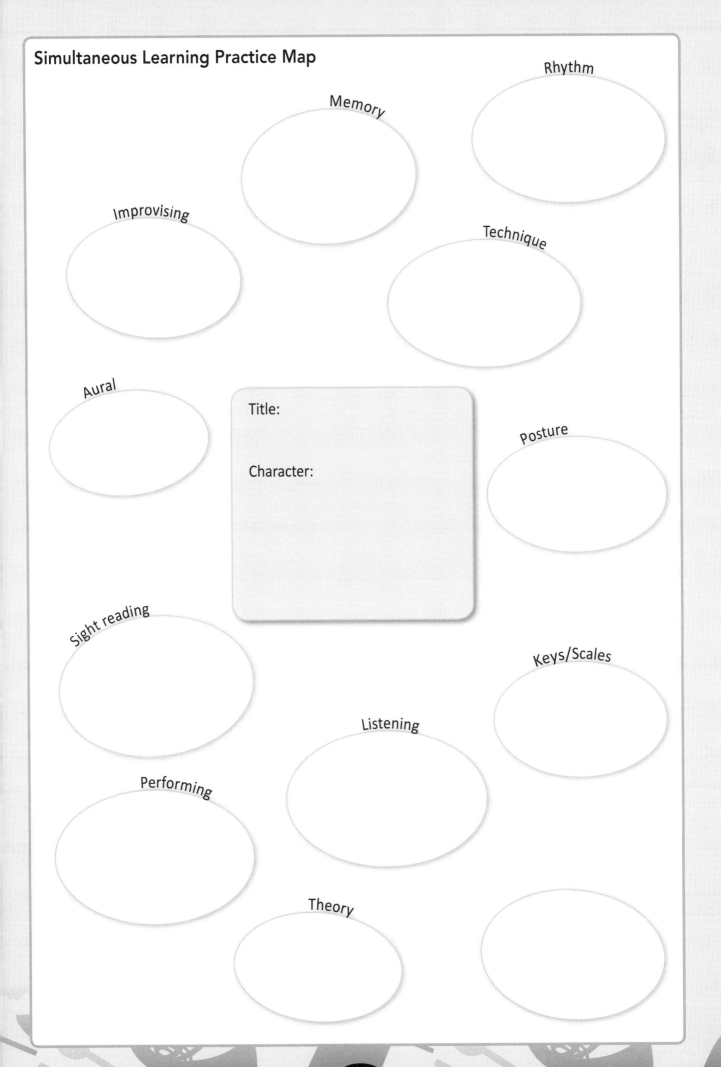

Rhythm

Memory

Improvising

Technique

Aural

Title:

Character:

Posture

Sight reading

Keys/Scales

Listening

Performing

Theory

© 2014 by Faber Music Ltd
This edition first published in 2014
Bloomsbury House
74–77 Great Russell Street
London WC1B 3DA
Designed by Susan Clarke
Printed in England by Caligraving Ltd
All rights reserved

ISBN10: 0-571-59734-3
EAN13: 978-0-571-59734-5

To buy Faber Music publications or to find out about the full range of titles available
please contact your local music retailer or Faber Music sales enquiries:

Faber Music Limited, Burnt Mill, Elizabeth Way, Harlow, CM20 2HX England
Tel: +44 (0)1279 82 89 82   Fax: +44 (0)1279 82 89 83
sales@fabermusic.com   fabermusicstore.com